MIND
-FUL-
NESS
colouring

Illustrations by
Holly Macdonald

QUADRILLE

INTRODUCTION

The pace of the world has changed, now fast moving, we are constantly surrounded by digital devices and with knowledge at our fingertips, it's easy to fall out of touch with a sense of reality. Often overwhelmed and weighed down by modern pressures, we can lose sight of the present as our focus lingers on regrets in the past and worries for the future.

Founded 2,600 years ago, the practice of mindfulness has been proven to contribute to feeling more satisfied in life, with theorised benefits including objectivity, enhanced equanimity, improved emotional intelligence and mental clarity, therefore making it easier to savour pleasures as they occur and helping you to become fully engaged with the here and now.

Mindfulness Colouring will help you get back in touch with the present, through a selection of 45 illustrations of the natural world, accompanied by a collection of mindful quotes, which will create a sense of inner peace. This soothing activity book, will guide you to explore your creative side, switch off, relax your mind and spirit as you find calm through colouring in.

"To live is the rarest thing in the world.
Most people just exist."

Oscar Wilde

"Try to learn to breathe deeply, really taste your food when you eat, and when you sleep, really sleep. Try as much as possible to be wholly alive with all your might, and when you laugh, laugh like hell. And when you get angry, get good and angry. Try to be alive. You will be dead soon enough."

Ernest Hemingway

"Your vision will become clear
only when you look into your heart.
Who looks outside, dreams.
Who looks inside, awakens."

Carl Jung

"Paradise is not a place; it's
a state of consciousness."

Sri Chinmoy

"You must live in the present, launch yourself on every wave, find your eternity in each moment. Fools stand on their island of opportunities and look toward another land. There is no other land; there is no other life but this."

Henry David Thoreau

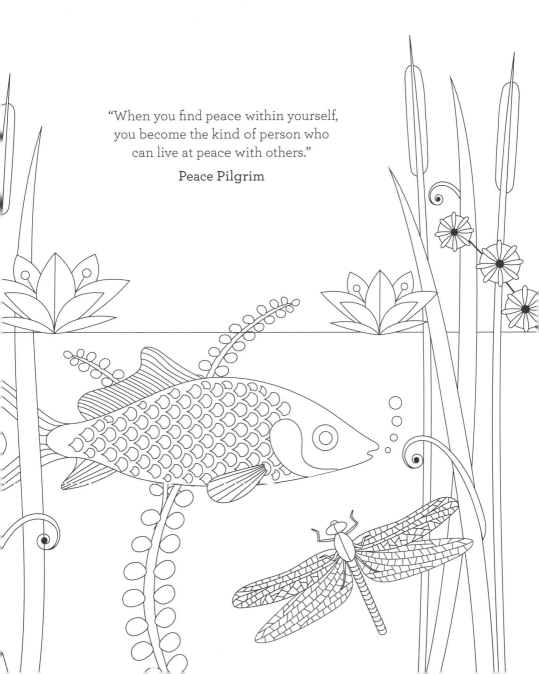

"When you find peace within yourself,
you become the kind of person who
can live at peace with others."

Peace Pilgrim

"Within you there is a stillness
and a sanctuary to which
you can retreat any time."

Hermann Hesse

"Feelings come and go like clouds in a windy sky. Conscious breathing is my anchor."

Thich Nhat Hanh
Stepping into Freedom

"Do every act of your life as
though it were your last."

Marcus Aurelius

"Don't let your happiness depend on
something you may lose."

C S Lewis

"The best thing about the future is that it only comes one day at a time."

Abraham Lincoln

"Breath is the bridge which connects life
to consciousness, which unites your body
to your thoughts. Whenever your mind
becomes scattered, use your breath as the
means to take hold of your mind again.

Thich Nhat Hanh
The Miracle of Mindfulness

"True happiness, we are told, consists in getting out of one's self; but the point is not only to get out — you must stay out, you must have some absorbing errand."

Henry James
Roderick Hudson

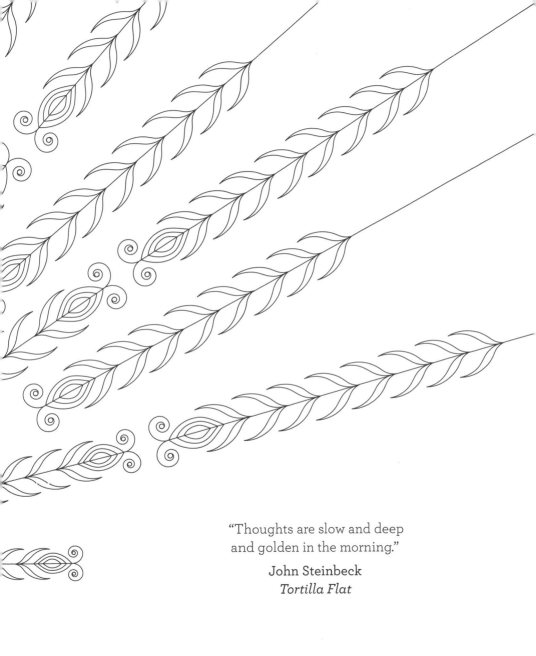

"Thoughts are slow and deep
and golden in the morning."

John Steinbeck
Tortilla Flat

"Always hold fast to the present. Every situation, indeed every moment is of infinite value, for it is the representative of a whole eternity."

Johann Wolfgang von Goethe

"Mindfulness is about being fully awake in our lives. It is about perceiving the exquisite vividness of each moment. We also gain immediate access to our own powerful inner resources for insight, transformation, and healing."

Jon Kabat-Zinn

"Begin doing what you want to do now. We are not living in eternity. We only have this moment, sparkling like a star in our hand and melting like a snowflake."

Sir Francis Bacon

"People have a hard
time letting go of their
suffering. Out of a fear of
the unknown, they prefer
suffering that is familiar."

Thich Nhat Hanh

"Dare to live the life you have
dreamed for yourself. Go forward
and make your dreams come true."

Ralph Waldo Emerson

"Mindfulness is a state of active, open attention in the present. When you're mindful, you observe your thoughts and feelings from a distance, without judging them good or bad. Instead of letting your life pass you by, mindfulness means living in the moment and awakening to experience."

Psychology Today

"Let us spend one day as deliberately as nature, and not be thrown off track by every nutshell and mosquito's wing that falls on the rails. Let us rise early and fast, or break fast, gently and without perturbation; let company come and let company go, let the bells ring and the children cry, — determine to make a day of it."

Henry David Thoreau

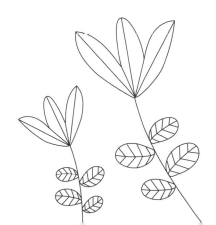

"The world is full of magic things, patiently
waiting for our sense to grow sharper."

W B Yeats

"Be content with what you have,
rejoice in the way things are. When
you realise there is nothing lacking, the
whole world belongs to you."

Lao Tzu

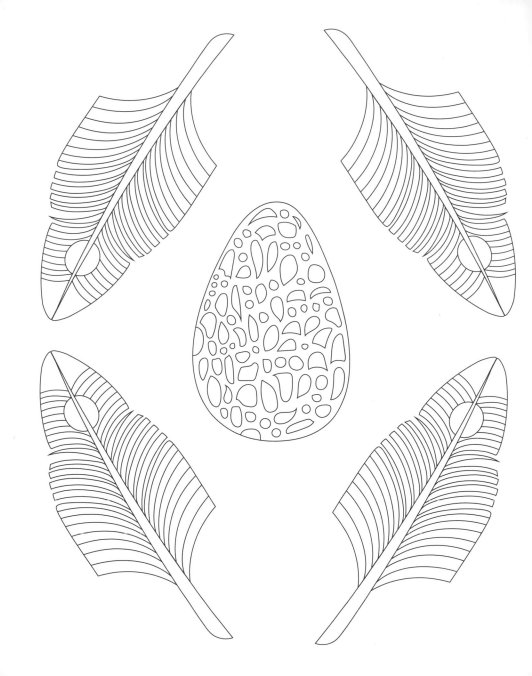

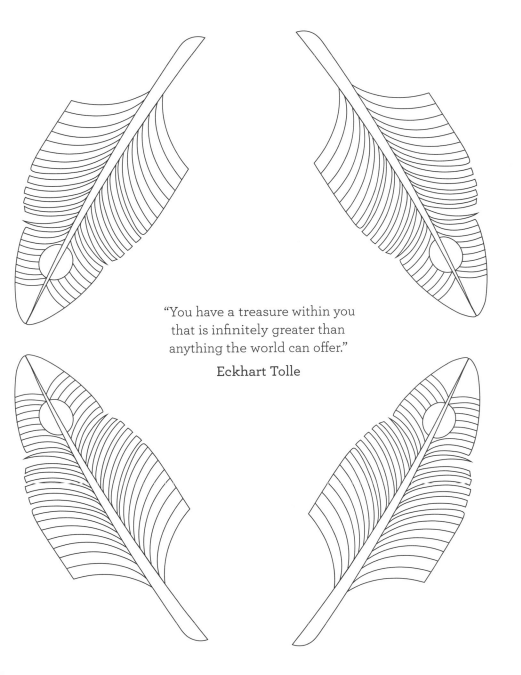

"You have a treasure within you
that is infinitely greater than
anything the world can offer."

Eckhart Tolle

"Mindfulness helps you go home to the present. And every time you go there and recognise a condition of happiness that you have, happiness comes."

Thich Nhat Hanh

"Seize every moment its
unique novelty, and do not
prepare your joys."

André Gide
Les Nourritures Terrestres

"Perfection of character is this:
to live each day as if it were your
last, without frenzy, without
apathy, without pretence."

Marcus Aurelius
Meditations

"The most precious gift we can
offer others is our presence. When
mindfulness embraces those we love,
they bloom like flowers."

Thich Nhat Hanh

"Discovery consists not in seeking new lands
but in seeing with new eyes."

Marcel Proust

BIBLIOGRAPHY

Books mentioned in
Mindfulness Colouring

Aurelius, Marcus., *Meditations*
(Penguin Classics, 2006)

Gide, André., *Les Nourritures Terrestres*
(Gallimard, 1977)

Hanh, Thich Nhat., *Stepping into Freedom:
An Introduction to Buddhist Monastic Training*
(Parallax, 1997)

Hanh, Thich Nhat., *The Miracle of Mindfulness:
An Introduction to the Practice of Meditation*
(Beacon Press, 1996)

James, Henry., *Roderick Hudson* (Penguin
Classics, 1986)

Pilgrim, Peace., *Peace Pilgrim: Her Life
and Work in Her Own Words*
(Ocean Tree Books, 1998)

Steinbeck, John., *Tortilla Flat* (Penguin
Classics, 1997)

Website

Psychology Today. Available at:
www.psychologytoday.com

Further reading

Farrarons, Emma. *The Mindfulness Colouring
Book: Anti-stress art therapy for busy people*
(Boxtree, 2015)

Rowan, Tiddy. *Colour Yourself Calm: A
Mindfulness Colouring Book* (Quadrille, 2014)

Rowan, Tiddy. *The Little Book of Confidence*
(Quadrille, 2015)

Rowan, Tiddy. *The Little Book of Quiet*
(Quadrille, 2014)

Rowan, Tiddy. *The Little Book of Mindfulness*
(Quadrille, 2013)

Sweet, Corinne. *The Mindfulness Journal:
Exercises to help you find peace and calm
wherever you are* (Boxtree, 2014)

Williams, Mark. *Mindfulness: A practical guide to
finding peace in a frantic world* (Platkus, 2011)

Apps

www.calm.com

www.getsomeheadspace.com

www.stopbreathethink.org

The Mindfulness Training App

Mindfulness Bell

QUOTES ARE TAKEN FROM

Abraham Lincoln was the 16th president of the United States of America. He preserved the Union during U.S. Civil War and brought about the emancipation of slaves.

André Gide was a French author, known for his fiction, which was often seen as an investigation of freedom. He won the Nobel Prize for Literature in 1947.

Carl Jung was a revolutionary psychiatrist and psychotherapist. He is best known for having founded analytical psychology.

C S Lewis was one of the literary giants of the twentieth century. His most renowned books are *The Chronicles of Narnia* series and *The Screwtape Letters*.

Eckhart Tolle is a spiritual writer and author of *The Power of Now*.

Ernest Hemingway was an American author and journalist. He won the Nobel prize in literature in 1954.

Francis Bacon was an English philosopher, statesman and a pioneer of modern scientific thought. He was the son of Sir Nicolas Bacon and keeper of the great seal for Elizabeth I.

Henry James was an American-born author and literary critic and brother of the psychologist and philosopher William James.

Hermann Hesse was a German-born Swiss poet, novelist, and painter.

Henry David Thoreau was an American author, poet and philosopher.

Johann Wolfgang von Goethe was a German writer and statesman and is considered the greatest German literary figure.

John Steinbeck was an American novelist who was best known for his novels *Of Mice and Men* and *The Grapes of Wrath*. He was awarded the Nobel Prize for Literature in 1962.

Jon Kabat-Zinn is a Professor of Medicine Emeritus and creator of the Centre for Mindfulness in Medicine.

Lao Tzu was a philosopher and poet of ancient China and author of *Tao Te Ching*.

Marcel Proust was a French novelist best known for his monumental novel *Remembrance of Things Past*.

Marcus Aurelius was Roman Emperor from 161 to 180 and was considered one of the most important Stoic philosophers.

Oscar Wilde was an Irish writer, playwright and poet. He is best known for his book *The Picture of Dorian Gray*.

Socrates was a classical Greek Philosopher.

Sri Chinmoy was an Indian spiritual master who taught mediation.

Ralph Waldo Emerson was an American preacher, philosopher, lecturer and poet, and the leader of the Transcendentalist movement.

Thich Nhat Hanh is a Zen Buddhist monk, author, and one of the leading spiritual teachers.

W.B. Yeats was an Irish poet who was awarded the Nobel Prize for literature in 1923.

PAGE REFERENCES

Page 21: Peace Pilgrim, *Peace Pilgrim: Her Life and Work in Her Own Words* (Ocean Tree Books, 1998)

Page 27: Thich Nhat Hanh, *Stepping into Freedom: An Introducion to Buddhist Monastic Training* (Parallax, 1997)

Page 43: Thich Nhat Hanh, *The Miracle of Mindfulness: An Introduction to the Practice of Meditation* (Beacon Press, 1996)

Page 45: Henry James, *Roderick Hudson* (Penguin Classics, 1986)

Page 47: John Steinbeck, *Tortilla Flat* (Penguin Classics, 1997)

Page 85: André Gide, *Les Nourritures Terrestres* (Gallimard, 1977)

Page 87: Marcus Aurelius, *Meditations* (Penguin Classics, 2006)

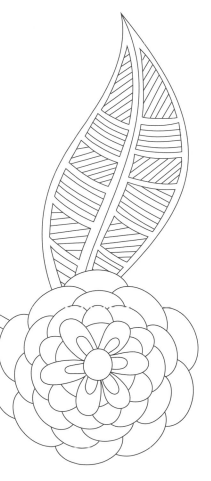

Illustrator Holly Macdonald
Publishing director Sarah Lavelle
Commissioning editor Lisa Pendreigh
Editorial assistant Harriet Butt
Creative director Helen Lewis
Senior designer Claire Peters
Designer Emily Lapworth
Production director Vincent Smith
Production controller Emily Noto

First published in 2015 by
Quadrille Publishing Ltd
Pentagon House
52-54 Southwark Street
London SE1 1UN
www.quadrille.co.uk

Compilation, design and layout
© 2015 Quadrille Publishing Ltd
Illustrations © 2015 Holly
MacDonald

Quadrille is an imprint
of Hardie Grant
www.hardiegrant.com.au

British Library Cataloguing-
in-Publication Data
A catalogue record for this book is
available from the British Library.

ISBN: 978 1 84949 724 4

Printed in China